PIANO TOWN
Level 4 • Theory
By Keith Snell & Diane Hidy

Contents

ISBN 0-8497-7333-4

© **2004 Kjos Music Press**, 4382 Jutland Drive, San Diego, California.

Use with *Lessons*, page 4.

Triads and Inversions

Root Position	First Inversion	Second Inversion

Root on the bottom	**3rd** on the bottom	**5th** on the bottom

1. Draw the inversions for each root position triad. Play these chords.

Root Position	**First Inversion**	**Second Inversion**

D

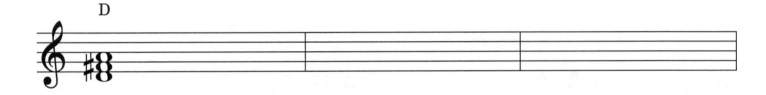

B♭

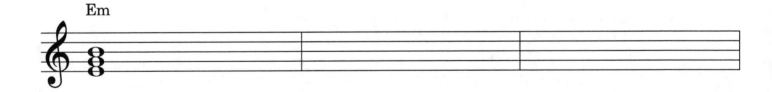

Em

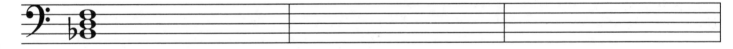

Am

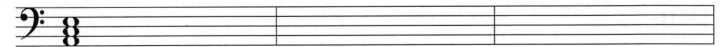

MP114

Identifying Inverted Triads

Triads in **first inversion** have the intervals of a 6th and a 3rd.

The root is on the top.

6th   +   3rd   =   1st Inversion

2. These triads are in first inversion. Color in the root (top note) then write the name of the triad. Play these chords.

Triads in **second inversion** have the intervals of a 6th and a 4th.

The root is in the middle.

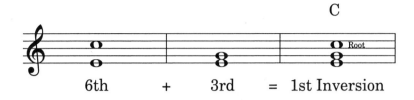

6th   +   4th   =   2nd Inversion

3. These triads are in second inversion. Color in the root (middle note) then write the name of the triad. Play these chords.

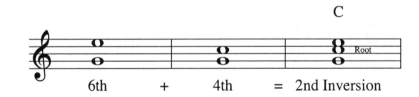

MP114

3

V7 Chords and Inversions

The V7 chord is built on the 5th degree of the scale. V7 chords have three inversions.
In an inverted V7 chord, the root is always the top note of the interval of a 2nd.

Key of C Major

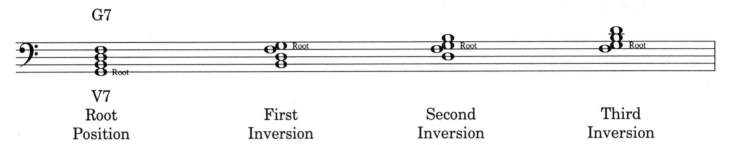

4.   Draw the inversions of these root position V7 chords. Play them.

5.   Color in the root of each chord (top note of the interval of a 2nd).
     Write the chord name on the line above the staff.
     Name the key to which each chord belongs on the line below the staff. Play these chords.

Intervals of the Scale

The intervals of the C Major scale are shown below.
Each interval is formed from the **tonic** (first) note of the scale.

There are two types, or **qualities** of intervals formed in this way:
1. **Major** (2nd, 3rd, 6th and 7th)
2. **Perfect** (4th, 5th and octave)

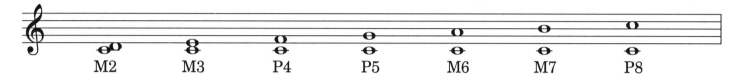

M2   M3   P4   P5   M6   M7   P8

These interval qualities are the same for any Major scale.

6. Name these intervals of the B♭ Major scale. Play them.

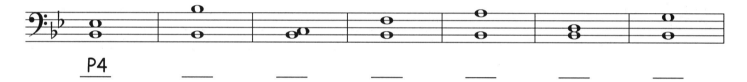

P4 ___ ___ ___ ___ ___ ___

7. Name these intervals of the F Major scale. Play them.

M2 ___ ___ ___ ___ ___ ___

8. Name these intervals of the A Major scale. Play them.

___ ___ ___ ___ ___ ___ ___

Major and Minor Intervals

Major intervals become minor when
the top note is lowered one half step.

Key of C Major

9. Draw a minor interval after each Major interval. Observe the key signature and
   use a flat or natural sign as needed. Play these intervals.

Key of D Major

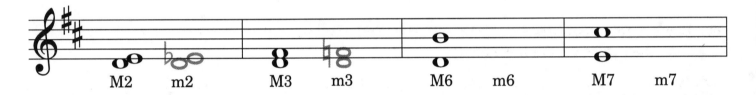

Key of G Major

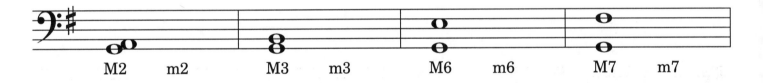

10. Name each interval. play them.

Key of F Major

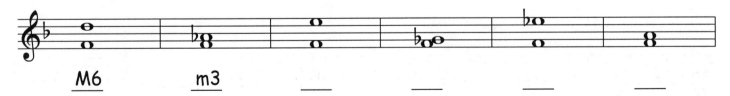

Key of B♭ Major

MP114

Diminished and Augmented Intervals

Perfect intervals become **diminished** when the top note is **lowered** one half step.

Perfect intervals become **Augmented** when the top note is **raised** one half step.

11. Draw a note above the one given to form a Perfect, diminished or Augmented interval. Play the intervals you have drawn.

12. Name each interval. Play them

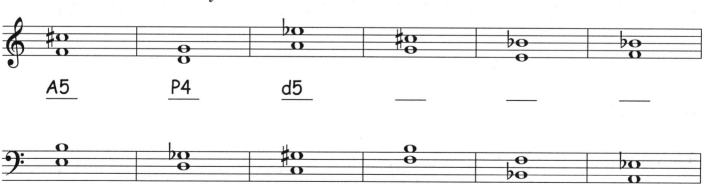

Use with *Lessons*, page 10 and 11.

Diminished Triads

The word *diminish* means "to make smaller."

Diminished triads are formed by lowering the 5th of a minor triad one half step.

Diminished triads in root position have the intervals of a diminished 5th and minor 3rd.

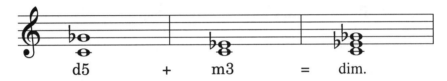

13. Draw a diminished triad after each minor triad. Play these triads.

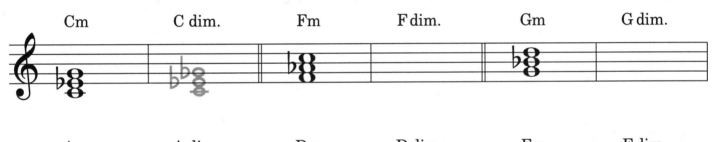

14. Draw the inversions for each root position diminished triad. Play them.

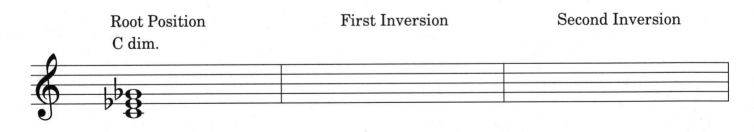

Augmented Triads

The word *augment* means "to make bigger."

Augmented triads are formed by raising the 5th of a Major triad one half step.

Augmented triads in root position have the intervals of an Augmented 5th and Major 3rd.

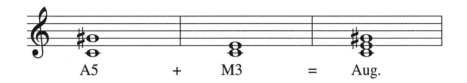

15. Draw an Augmented triad after each Major triad. Play these triads.

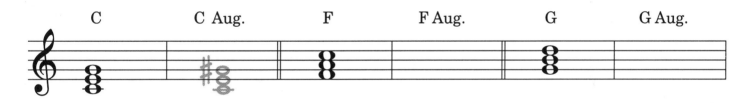

16. Draw the inversions for each root position Augmented triad. Play them.

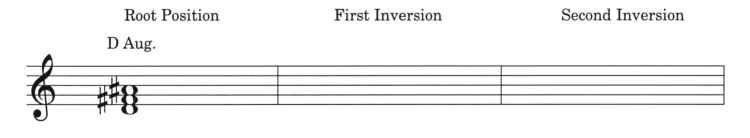

Sixteenth Notes

17. Add two more barlines to this rhythm. Write the counts on the line below the notes.
    Clap and count aloud.

    1   2

18. Add one barline to this rhythm. Write the counts.
    Clap and count aloud.

19. Add three barlines to this rhythm. Write the counts.
    Clap and count aloud.

20. Add three barlines to this rhythm. Write the counts.
    Clap and count aloud.

Scale Degrees

Each degree of a scale has a name.

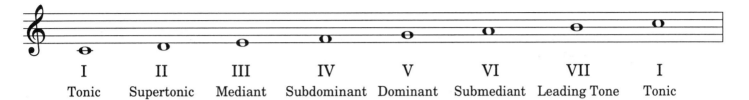

I	II	III	IV	V	VI	VII	I
Tonic	Supertonic	Mediant	Subdominant	Dominant	Submediant	Leading Tone	Tonic

Each scale degree name refers to its position up or down from the tonic.

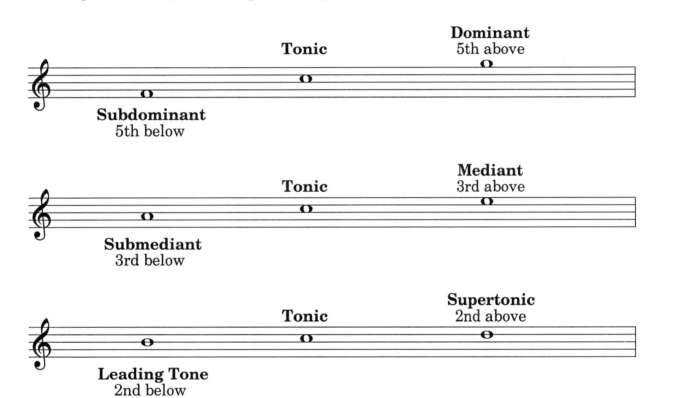

21. Write the scale degree name for each note of the F Major scale.

Tonic _____ _____ _____ _____ _____ _____

22. Draw the note for each scale degree name of the G Major scale.

Tonic   Dominant   Mediant   Leading Tone   Subdominant   Supertonic   Submediant

Triads of Major Scales

A triad may be built on each degree of the Major scale.

Each triad is labeled with a Roman numeral and named after the scale degree of its root.
Upper or lower case Roman numerals indicate the quality of the triad:

Major: upper case
minor: lower case
diminished: lower case and °

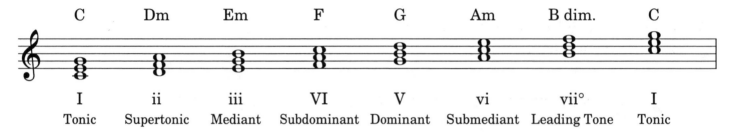

C	Dm	Em	F	G	Am	B dim.	C
I	ii	iii	VI	V	vi	vii°	I
Tonic	Supertonic	Mediant	Subdominant	Dominant	Submediant	Leading Tone	Tonic

These triad qualities are the same for any Major scale.

23. Write the Roman numeral below each triad of the D Major scale.
    Write the chord name above the staff. Play these chords.

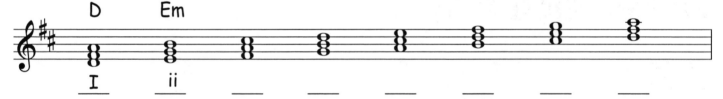

24. Write the Roman numeral below each triad of the B♭ Major scale.
    Write the chord name above the staff. Play these chords.

25. Draw each triad of the E Major scale according to the degree name.
    Write the Roman numeral below each triad.
    Write the chord name above the staff. Play these chords.

Tonic   Dominant   Mediant   Leading Tone   Supertonic   Subdominant   Submediant

     MP114

Sixteenth Rest

26.   Trace the first sixteenth rest, then draw four more.

3/8

27. Add three barlines to this rhythm. Write the counts.
    Clap and count aloud.

Dotted Eighth Note

28. Add three barlines to this rhythm. Write the counts.
    Clap and count aloud.

The Order of Flats

The flats in key signatures
are always in the same order.

Memorize the order of flats.

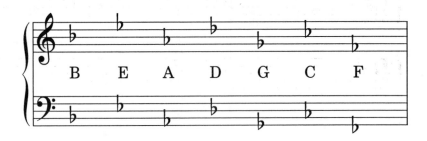

29. Trace the order of flats in the first measure,
    then draw the order of flats two more times.

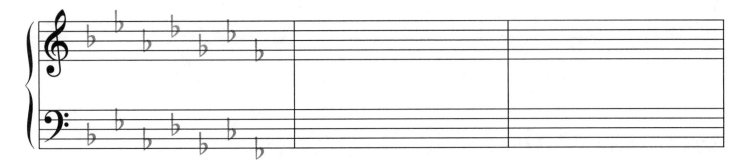

Naming Major Flat Key Signatures

To recognize and name any Major flat key signature,
name the next to last flat in the key signature.

The name of the next to last flat
is the name of the Major key.*

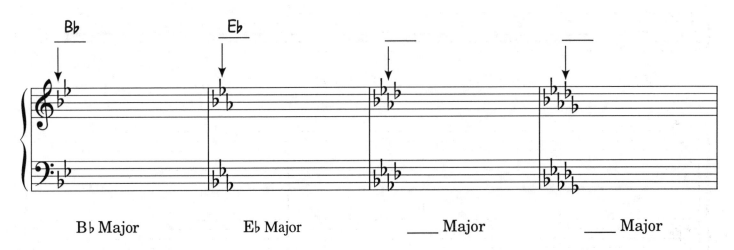

B♭ Major   E♭ Major   ____ Major   ____ Major

*Exception: the key of F Major has one flat, B♭.

30. Name these Major key signatures.

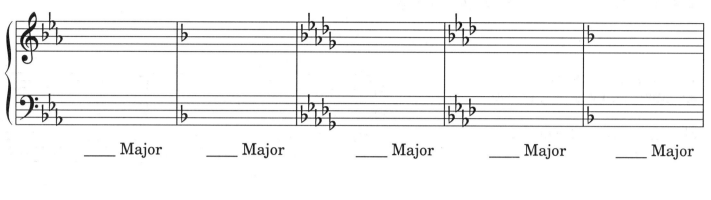

_____ Major   _____ Major   _____ Major   _____ Major   _____ Major

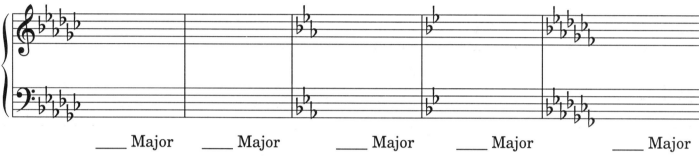

_____ Major   _____ Major   _____ Major   _____ Major   _____ Major

Writing Major Flat Key Signatures

To write the key signature for any Major flat key:
- Write the order of flats up to and including the flat after the tonic. (The tonic names the key.)

Example: Key of A♭ Major
Flat after tonic.

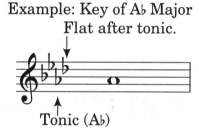

Tonic (A♭)

31. Write these Major key signatures.

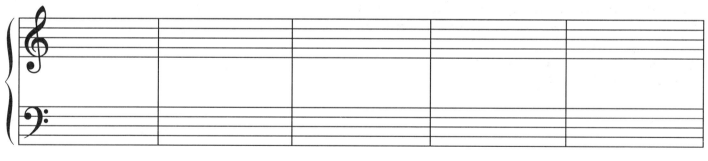

F Major   A♭ Major   B♭ Major   G♭ Major   E♭ Major

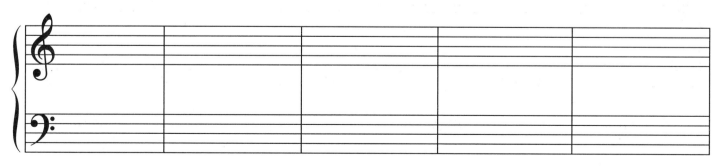

D♭ Major   C♭ Major   E♭ Major   A♭ Major   B♭ Major

E♭ Major Key Signature

The key signature for E♭ Major has three flats: B♭, E♭ and A♭.

32. Trace the first key signature, then draw two more.

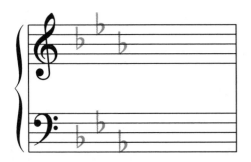  

E♭ Major Scale

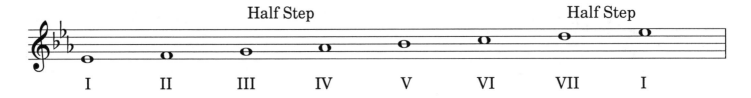

33. Draw the notes of the E♭ Major scale going **up**. Use quarter notes.
    Circle the half steps. Play the scale with your right hand.

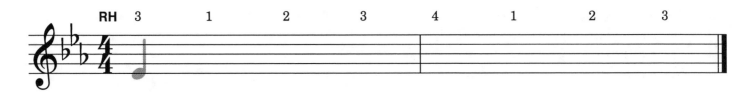

34. Draw the notes of the E♭ Major scale going **down**. Use quarter notes.
    Circle the half steps. Play the scale with your left hand.

Primary Chords in E♭ Major

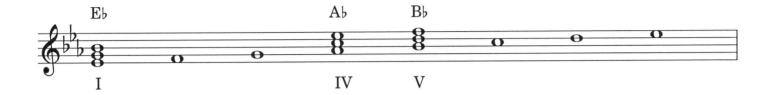

35. Draw the primary chords in E♭ Major in the treble and bass staff.
    Use whole notes. Play them.

Primary Chord Progression in E♭ Major

Shown below are the primary chords as they
will be used in the primary chord progression.

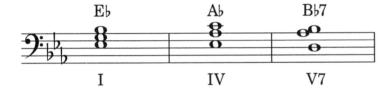

36. Play this melody and decide which chord sounds best in each measure: I, IV, or V7.
    Draw the chords in the bass staff. Use dotted quarter notes.
    Write Roman numerals below the staff.
    Write the name of each chord above the staff.

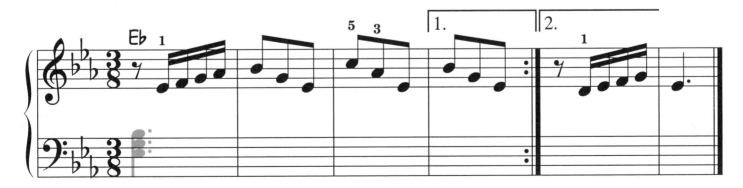

A♭ Major Key Signature

The key signature for A♭ Major has four flats: B♭, E♭, A♭, and D♭.

37. Trace the first key signature, then draw two more.

A♭ Major Scale

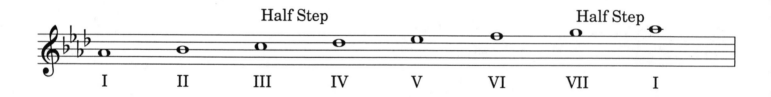

38. Draw the notes of the A♭ Major scale going **up**. Use quarter notes.
    Circle the half steps. Play the scale with your right hand.

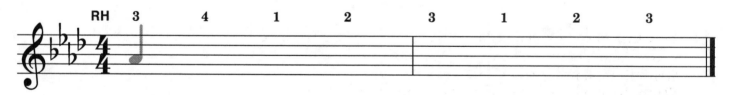

39. Draw the notes of the A♭ Major scale going **down**. Use quarter notes.
    Circle the half steps. Play the scale with your left hand.

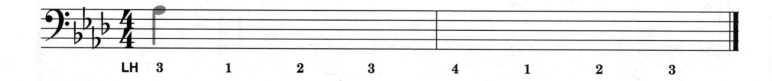

MP114

Primary Chords in A♭ Major

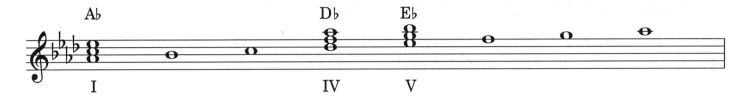

40. Draw the primary chords in A♭ Major in the treble and bass staff.
    Use whole notes. Play them.

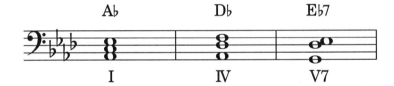

Primary Chord Progression in A♭ Major

Shown below are the primary chords as they
will be used in the primary chord progression.

41. Play this melody and decide which chord sounds best in each measure: I, IV, or V7.
    Draw the chords in the bass staff. Use half notes.
    Write Roman numerals below the staff.
    Write the name of each chord above the staff.

D♭ Major Key Signature

The key signature for D♭ Major has five flats: B♭, E♭, A♭, D♭, and G♭.

42. Trace the first key signature, then draw two more.

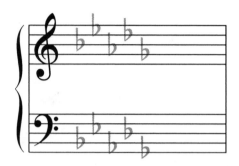  

D♭ Major Scale

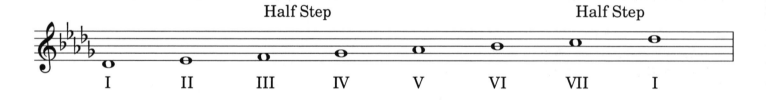

Half Step   Half Step

I   II   III   IV   V   VI   VII   I

43. Draw the notes of the D♭ Major scale going **up**. Use quarter notes.
Circle the half steps. Play the scale with your right hand.

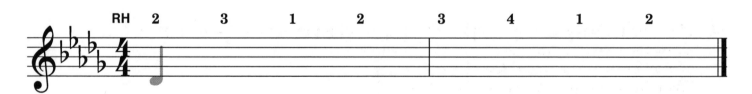

44. Draw the notes of the D♭ Major scale going **down**. Use quarter notes.
Circle the half steps. Play the scale with your left hand.

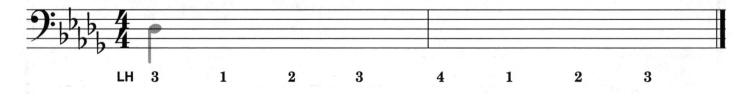

         MP114

Primary Chords in D♭ Major

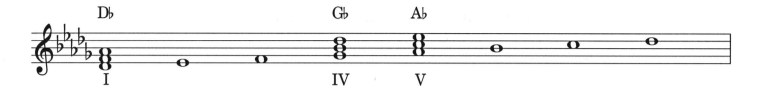

45. Draw the primary chords in D♭ Major in the treble and bass staff.
    Use whole notes. Play them.

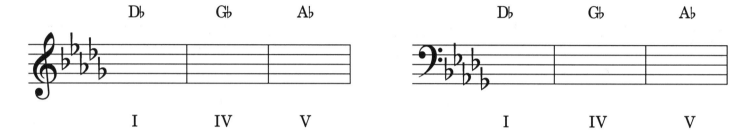

Primary Chord Progression in D♭ Major

Shown below are the primary chords as they
will be used in the primary chord progression.

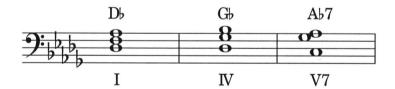

46. Play this melody and decide which chord sounds best in each measure: I, IV, or V7.
    Draw the chords in the bass staff. Use whole notes.
    Write Roman numerals below the staff.
    Write the name of each chord above the staff.

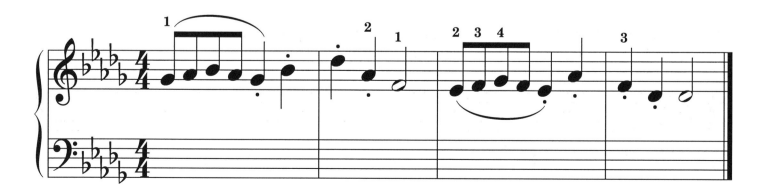

Use with *Lessons*, pages 32 -34.

G♭ Major Key Signature

The key signature for G♭ Major has six flats: B♭, E♭, A♭, D♭, G♭, and C♭.

47. Trace the first key signature, then draw two more.

G♭ Major Scale

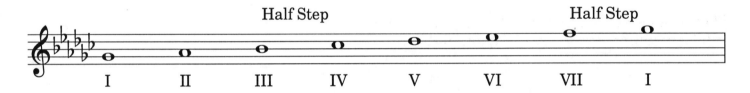

48. Draw the notes of the G♭ Major scale going **up**. Use quarter notes.
    Circle the half steps. Play the scale with your right hand.

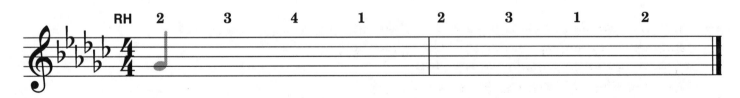

49. Draw the notes of the G♭ Major scale going **down**. Use quarter notes.
    Circle the half steps. Play the scale with your left hand.

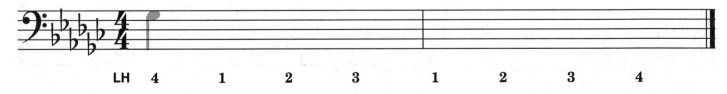

22

Primary Chords in G♭ Major

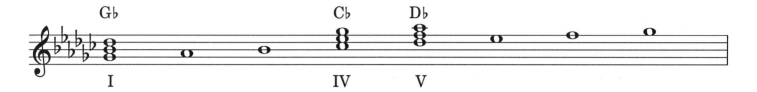

50. Draw the primary chords in G♭ Major in the treble and bass staff.
    Use whole notes. Play them.

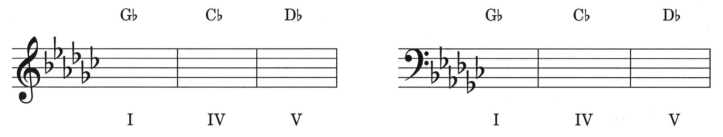

Primary Chord Progression in G♭ Major

Shown below are the primary chords as they
will be used in the primary chord progression.

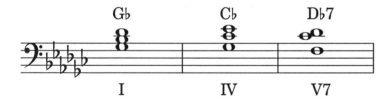

51. Play this melody and decide which chord sounds best in each measure: I, IV, or V7.
    Draw the chords in the bass staff. Use dotted half notes.
    Write Roman numerals below the staff.
    Write the name of each chord above the staff.

Use with *Lessons*, pages 35 - 37.

B Major Key Signature

The key signature for B Major has five sharps: F♯, C♯, G♯, D♯ and A♯.

52. Trace the first key signature, then draw two more.

B Major Scale

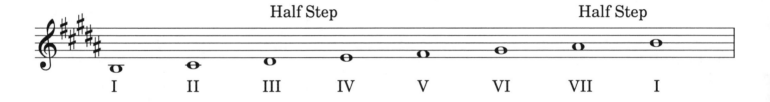

53. Draw the notes of the B Major scale going **up**. Use quarter notes.
    Circle the half steps. Play the scale with your right hand.

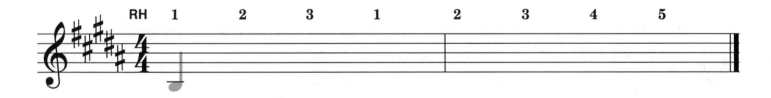

54. Draw the notes of the B Major scale going **down**. Use quarter notes.
    Circle the half steps. Play the scale with your left hand.

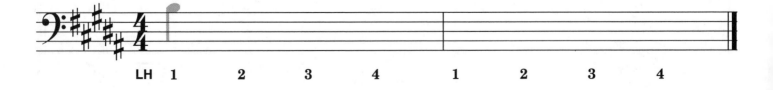

Primary Chords in B Major

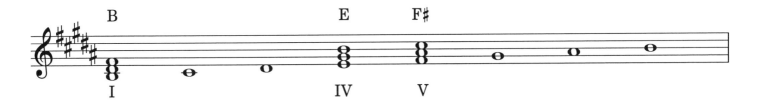

55. Draw the primary chords in B Major in the treble and bass staff.
    Use whole notes. Play them.

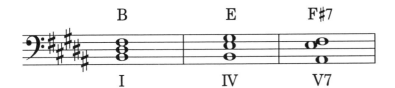

Primary Chord Progression in B Major

Shown below are the primary chords as they
will be used in the primary chord progression.

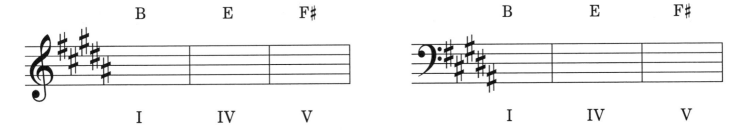

56. Play this melody and decide which chord sounds best in each measure: I, IV, or V7.
    Draw the chords in the bass staff. Use dotted half notes.
    Write Roman numerals below the staff.
    Write the name of each chord above the staff.

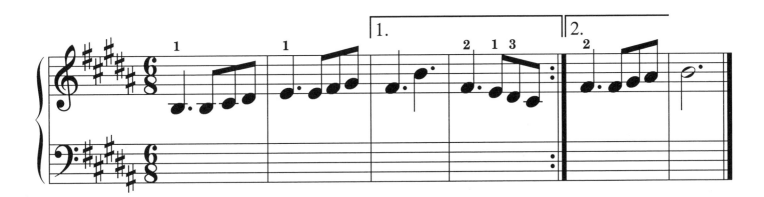

MP114

Order of Sharps Review

The sharps in key signatures are always in the same order.

Memorize the order of sharps.

57. Draw the order of sharps three times.

Order of Flats Review

The flats in key signatures are always in the same order.

Memorize the order of flats.

58. Draw the order of flats three times.

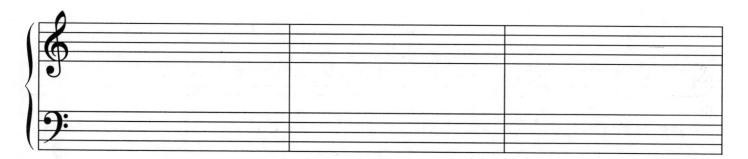

Writing Major Sharp Key Signatures

To write a Major sharp key signature:
- Name the sharp one half step below the tonic.
- Write the order of sharps up to and including the sharp that is one half step below the tonic.

Example: Key of E Major

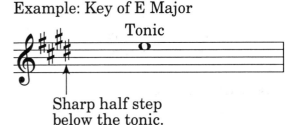

Sharp half step below the tonic.

59. Write these Major sharp key signatures.

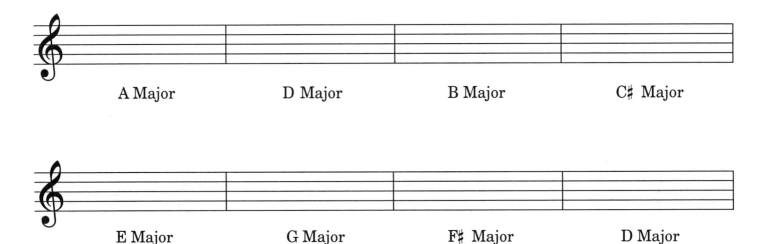

| A Major | D Major | B Major | C♯ Major |

| E Major | G Major | F♯ Major | D Major |

Writing Major Flat Key Signatures

To write a Major flat key signature:
- Write the order of flats up to and including the flat after the tonic.*

Example: Key of A♭ Major
Flat after tonic.

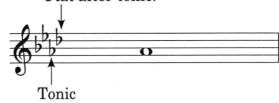

Tonic

60. Write these Major flat key signatures.

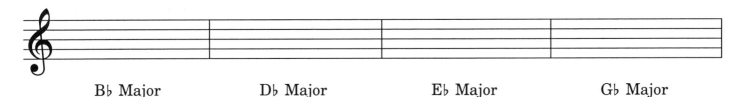

| B♭ Major | D♭ Major | E♭ Major | G♭ Major |

| A♭ Major | F Major | C♭ Major | B♭ Major |

*Exception: the key of F Major only has one flat, B♭.

Major and Minor Key Signatures

Every key signature has a Major and minor name.

D Major   B Minor

The minor key is found three half steps below the Major key.

F Major   D Minor

61. Write the Major and minor name for each key signature.

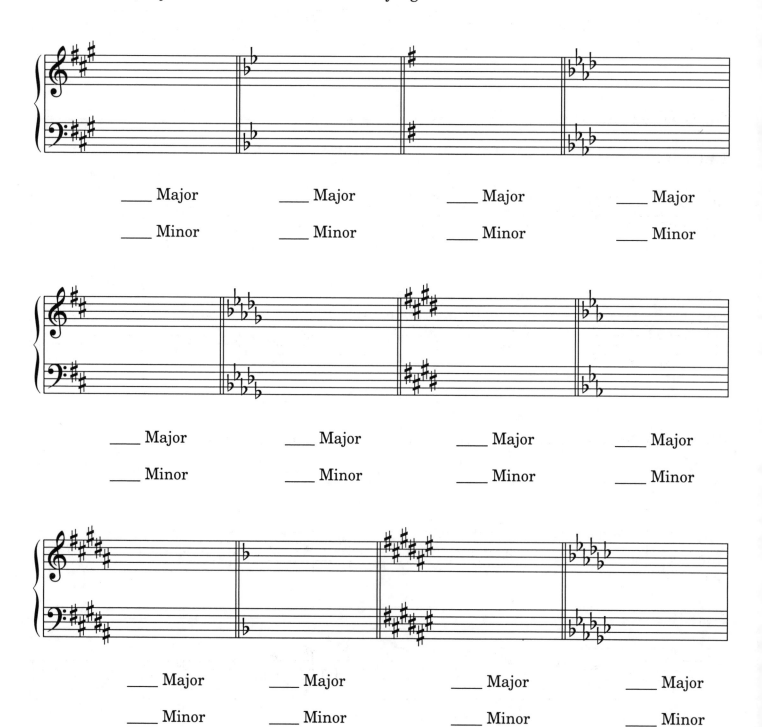

_____ Major   _____ Major   _____ Major   _____ Major

_____ Minor   _____ Minor   _____ Minor   _____ Minor

_____ Major   _____ Major   _____ Major   _____ Major

_____ Minor   _____ Minor   _____ Minor   _____ Minor

_____ Major   _____ Major   _____ Major   _____ Major

_____ Minor   _____ Minor   _____ Minor   _____ Minor

Minor Scale Review

62. Change these A natural minor scales to harmonic and melodic form.

Harmonic: raise the 7th degree one half step.

Melodic: raise the 6th and 7th degrees going up, then lower them coming down.

63. Change these E natural minor scales to harmonic and melodic form.

Harmonic

Melodic

64. Change these D natural minor scales to harmonic and melodic form.

Harmonic

Melodic

The Circle of Keys

The circle of keys is a diagram of all Major and minor key signatures. The sharp keys are arranged from the top, moving clockwise. The flats are arranged from the top moving counter clockwise.

There are fifteen Major keys: seven sharp keys, seven flat keys, and one key with no sharps or flats. Likewise, there are fifteen relative minor keys.

The keys at the bottom of the circle are called enharmonic keys because their tones sound the same, but are named and written differently.

The circle of keys is sometimes called the circle of fifths because the keys are arranged an interval of a fifth apart. Notice that as you move around the circle of keys clockwise from the top, one new sharp is added to each key. As you move counter clockwise from the top, one new flat is added to each key.

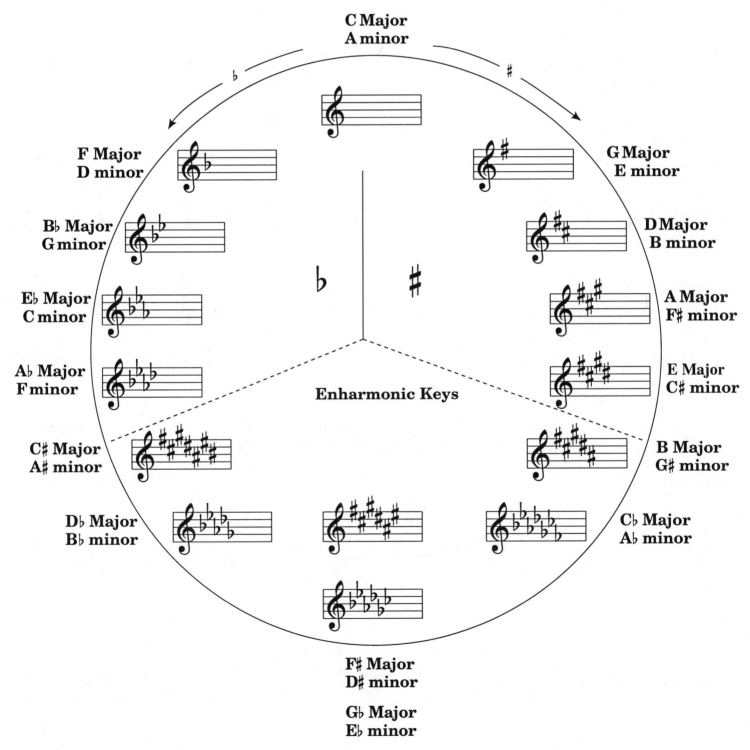

Writing the Circle of Keys

65. Write the name of each Major and minor key on the lines outside the circle.
    Write the sharps or flats for each key on the staffs inside the circle.

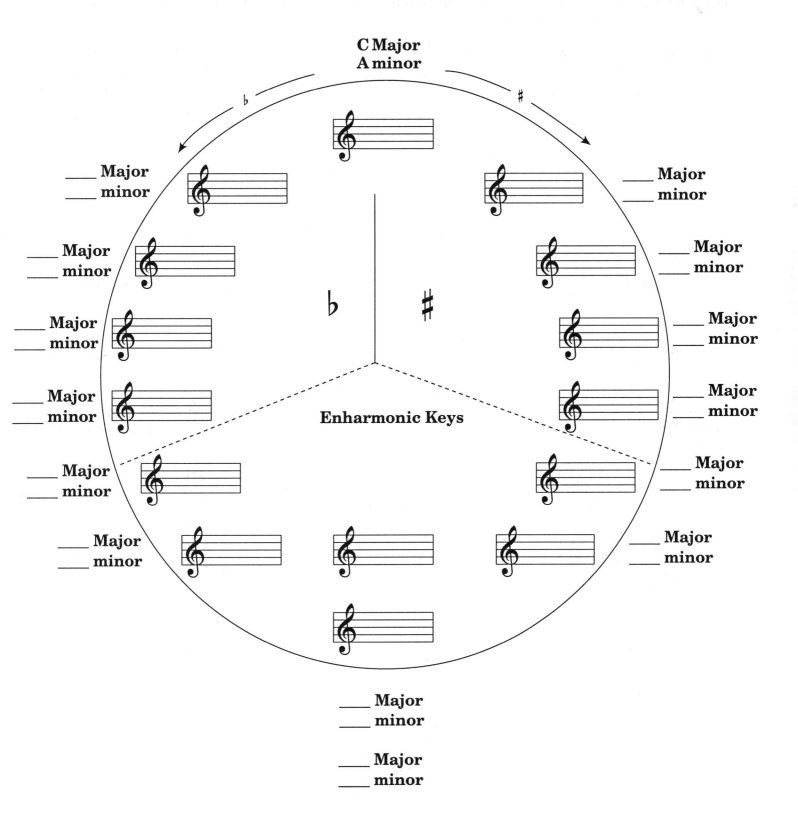

Music Dictionary

TERM	SIGN	MEANING
A tempo		Return to the original tempo.
Accent	>	Play the note or notes louder.
Alla breve (or "cut time")	¢	♩ = one beat.
Allegretto		Somewhat fast (slower than allegro).
Allegro		Fast.
Andante		Slow, walking tempo.
Binary Form		A piece with two sections: A and B.
Crescendo (cresc.)	◁	Gradually louder.
Da capo al fine (D.C. al Fine)		Go back to the beginning and play to the *Fine* (end).
Dal segno al fine (D.S. al Fine)		Go back to the sign (𝄋) and play to the *Fine*.
Diminuendo (dim.)	▷	Gradually softer.
Double Flat	♭♭	Lowers a note two half steps.
Double Sharp	𝄪	Raises a note two half steps.
Fermata	𝄐	Hold the note longer than its time value.
Flat	♭	Play the very next key lower.
Forte	*f*	Loud.
Interval		The distance between two notes.
Legato		Smoothly connected.
Mezzo forte	*mf*	Medium loud.
Mezzo piano	*mp*	Medium soft.
Moderato		Moderate speed.
Molto		Much, very.
Natural	♮	Cancels a sharp or flat.

MP114